Craft Book

ORCHARD BOOKS
338 Euston Road, London NW1 3BH

Orchard Books Australia
Level 17/207 Kent Street, Sydney, NSW 2000

First published in 2009 by Orchard Books.

All fairy illustrations on cover © Georgie Ripper, with the exception of Rihanna
the Seahorse Fairy. This illustration © Orchard Books 2009. All interior fairy
illustrations © Georgie Ripper, with the exception of Gabriella the Snow
Kingdom Fairy on page 10, Queen Titania on page 26 and Danni the Drum
Fairy on page 30. These illustrations © Orchard Books 2009.

With thanks to Rita Storey for all her help and creativity.

A CIP catalogue record for this book is available
from the British Library.

ISBN 978 1 40830 457 0

1 3 5 7 9 10 8 6 4 2

Printed in China
Orchard Books is a division of Hachette Children's Books,
an Hachette UK company

www.hachette.co.uk

Contents

Hello!

The Rainbow Magic fairies are here to add some sparkle to your day!

Inside they'll show you how to make beautiful fashion accessories, Christmassy decorations and yummy recipes straight from their own Fairyland cook books. Fairy fans everywhere are sure to be enchanted!

There are step-by-step pictures to help you, and a key at the top of each page shows you how easy or tricky the craft is to make. Just be sure to ask a grown-up before making any of these crafts!

Happy heart pendants

We love the necklaces that our Rainbow Magic fairy friends gave us. Here's how you can create your own heart necklace for a special friend – try red or gold or green or even rainbow-coloured. Be sure to make them super-sparkly too!

Rachel and Kirsty
xx

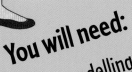

You will need:

Air-drying modelling clay
Pencil and paper
Scissors
Poster paints and paintbrush
Jewels or sequins to decorate
PVA glue
Thin ribbon

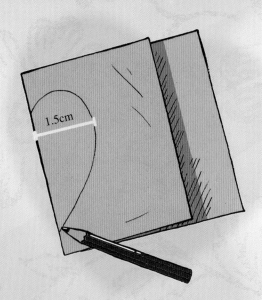

1.5cm

Step 1

Fold the paper in half. Against the folded side, draw half a heart so that it is 1.5cm across at the widest point. You may need an adult to help you.

Step 2

Cut out the heart and open it out. This will be the template for making your pendants. Roll out your clay to about 2mm thick.

Step 3

Place the heart on the clay and draw round it with a ballpoint pen or pencil. Remove the clay heart and gently smooth out the edges with your fingers.

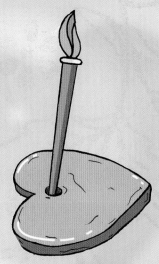

Step 4

Make a hole in the clay heart with the end of your paintbrush. Make sure that it goes all the way through the clay. Leave the clay to dry, then paint it a pretty colour or colours and leave it to dry again.

Step 5

Stick on jewels and sequins with PVA glue. Thread a colourful ribbon through the hole to make a necklace, or hang the heart in your room as a fun fairy decoration.

Perfect party bag

We Party Fairies would hardly have any magic at all if it wasn't for our seven enchanted party bags! Why not stitch your own little bag in your favourite fairy colours? You could fill it with sweet things, lipgloss or a pretty hairclip!

Grace
the Glitter Fairy
xx

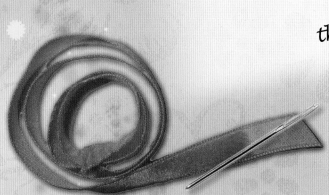

You will need:

50 square cm net fabric
34 square cm lining fabric
Scissors
Fabric glue
10 square cm card
A roll of thin elastic cord
Needle (suitable for threading elastic cord)
Approx 40 cm of coloured ribbon

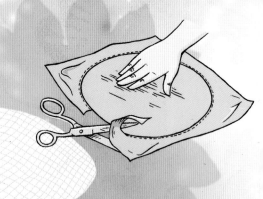

Step 1
Cut the net fabric into a circle that is about 22cm across the middle. Cut the lining fabric into a circle about 17cm across.

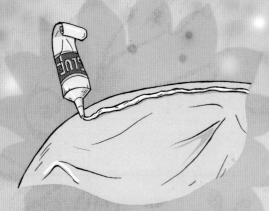

Step 2
Spread out the fabric circle on a flat surface. Squeeze a thin line of glue round the outer edge of the fabric.

Step 3
Stick the net circle on top of the fabric circle, leaving about 5cm of net around the edge. Allow the glue to dry.

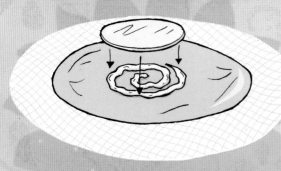

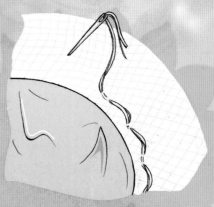

Step 4
Turn the circles over so the fabric is on top. Cut the card into a circle about 10cm across. Glue the card to the middle of the fabric circle.

Step 5
Use the needle to thread the elastic in and out of the net just outside the fabric circle. Pull the ends of the elastic tight and tie them together. Cut off the extra elastic.

Step 6
Cut two small holes in the net about 10cm apart. Thread the ribbon through the holes and tie into a bow. Use the ribbon as a handle for your party bag.

Pretty pirouetting tutu

Do you love to point your toes and dance? If you do, then this twinkly pink tutu could be just the thing to wear for your next performance. When you pop on the graceful net skirt you'll feel like the most beautiful ballerina in the world!

Bethany
the Ballet Fairy
xx

You will need:
1 metre of net fabric
Hole punch
1 metre of thin ribbon
Jewels and sequins (optional)
PVA glue

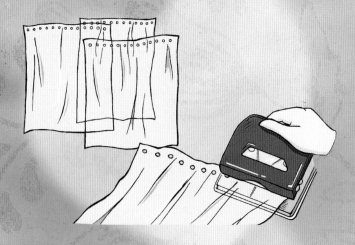

Step 1

Cut the net into four strips, each 25cm wide. Use the hole punch to make holes along the top of each strip. The holes should be about 2cm apart.

8

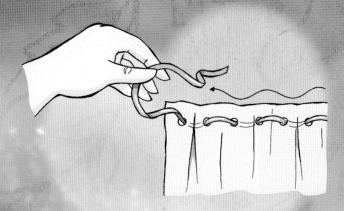

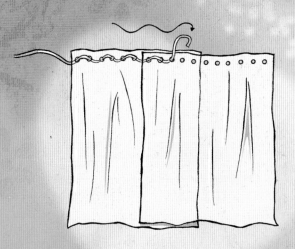

Step 2

Thread the ribbon in and out of the holes. This will be the waistband of your tutu.

Step 3

Join the strips of net by overlapping the last five holes of one strip with the first five holes of the next, and thread the ribbon through both strips.

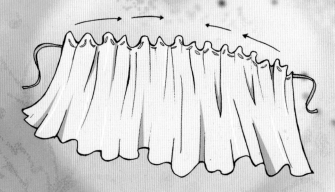

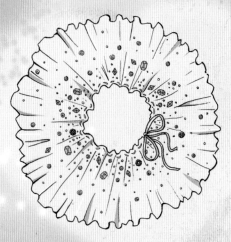

Step 4

When you've threaded the ribbon through all the holes, gently pull on both ends to gather the net until it fits round your waist. Leave an equal amount of ribbon at each end for a bow.

Step 5

Decorate your tutu by using a dab of PVA glue to stick jewels and sequins onto the net. (Make sure your decorations are not too heavy!) Leave to dry.

Step 6

Tie the ribbons into a pretty bow round your waist. Then leap and twirl, just like a prima ballerina!

Sparkly snowflake cards

These exquisite wintry cards will make your friends feel super-special! Each one has a unique snowflake design created just for them, plus a gorgeous gift bow in a pretty colour. As a finishing touch I use a matching glitter pen to write the message inside.

Gabriella
the Snow Kingdom Fairy
xx

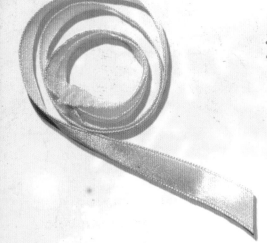

You will need:

2 sheets of white paper
Scissors
Coloured card (28cm x 14cm)
Coloured ribbon
PVA glue
Glitter
Plates or tins to help draw perfect circles (optional)
Newspaper

Step 1

Fold the card in half to make a square. Draw a circle on one half of the card and cut out. Set it aside to use later in Step 2. Smear a little glue on the front of the card (the side with the hole) and sprinkle on some glitter. Allow to dry.

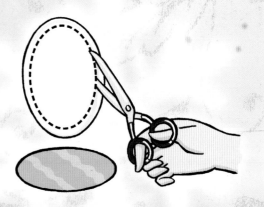

Step 2

Draw a smaller circle on the circle of card and cut out. Then use this smaller circle as a template to cut out a circle of white paper.

Step 3

Fold the circle of white paper in half and then in half again two or three more times. Cut out shapes, then unfold to reveal your snowflake.

Step 4

Use PVA glue to stick the snowflake onto the small circle of card. Allow to dry.

Step 5

Lay the card face down on newspaper. Centre the snowflake face down in the hole. Glue ribbon to the back of the snowflake and to the card above and below. Trim the extra ribbon.

Step 6

Glue a 14 square cm piece of white paper inside the card behind the snowflake. Use another ribbon to tie a pretty gift bow and glue it to the front of the card. Allow to dry, then write a message to your fairy friend inside!

Fairy charm rings

It's so hard to find jewellery to fit tiny fairy fingers! These little rings are very easy to make, and they can be threaded with all sorts of beads and buttons. When I put my rose-coloured one on, it makes my dress and party shoes look extra special.

*Scarlett
the Garnet Fairy
xx*

You will need:
A roll of thin elastic cord (either rainbow-coloured or sparkly is pretty!)
Selection of beads and buttons
Scissors

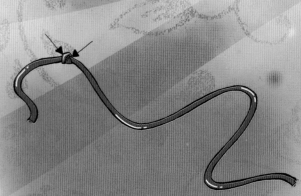

Step 1
Tie a knot in a piece of the elastic. Thread a small bead or button onto the elastic. Make sure the knot is big enough so the bead or button doesn't slip off.

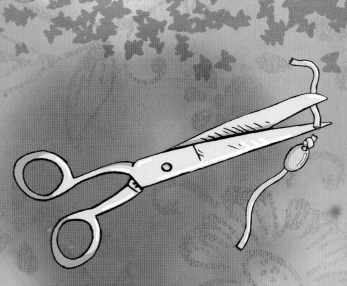

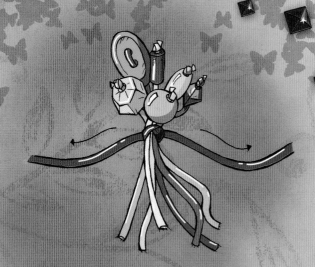

Step 2

Trim off the elastic above the knot. Repeat four or five times, using different coloured elastic and different beads or buttons.

Step 3

Use another piece of elastic to tie all the beads and buttons together into a bunch, leaving a long piece of elastic on either end.

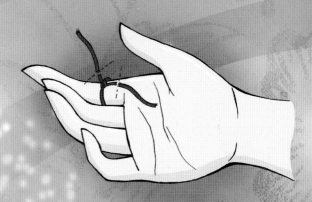

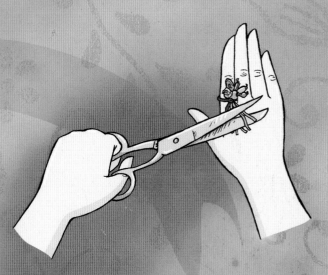

Step 4

Ask a grown-up to tie the long pieces of elastic round your finger. Make sure it isn't too tight! Tie a knot in the ring and cut off the elastic above the knot.

Step 5

Ask a grown-up to trim the elastic that the beads are threaded onto, so they are different lengths. Your ring will add that special fairy touch to any outfit!

Fairy tresses

Whenever I want to dress up my hair, I slide in this rainbow hair decoration! Don't worry if you've got short hair, the flowing ribbons set off any style. The clips are wonderful for when I'm performing – I like the way they flutter as I glide round the ice rink!

Imogen
the Ice Dance Fairy
xx

You will need:

Selection of rainbow-coloured ribbons, wool and lace

Small elastic band

Hairclip

Step 1

Cut a selection of rainbow–coloured ribbons, wool and lace to about 5cm longer than your hair.

Step 2

Bunch them together and secure with a small elastic band about 5cm below the top.

Step 3

Cut a piece of ribbon about 30cm long and clip it inside your hairclip.

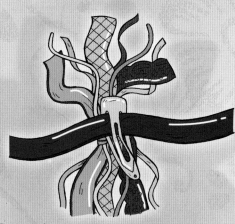

Step 4

Slide the back of the hairclip through the elastic band.

Step 5

Tie the long ribbon around the decoration and make a pretty bow at the front. Clip the fairy tresses into your hair or onto a ponytail.

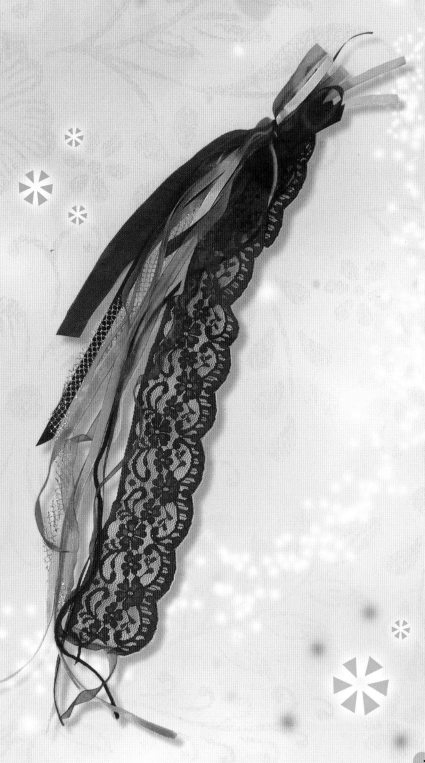

Fairly easy

Jewelled hairband

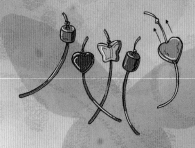

The feathers in this ponytail band turn everyday hair into something fairy fantastic! I use one to tie up my blonde curls — I love the way the beads match my amethyst necklace. How about making a decoration to go with your favourite party outfit?

Amy
the Amethyst Fairy
xx

Step 1
Cut a 6cm length of elastic for each bead. Tie a knot in each end. Thread on the bead and cut off the elastic above the knot.

Step 2
Add some ribbons and feathers to the beads to make a bunch. With a piece of narrow ribbon, tie the beads, feathers and ribbons tightly together.

You will need:
Thin elastic cord
(preferably in a pretty colour)
A ponytail band
Thin ribbon
Beads and feathers
(either rainbow colours or match the colours of your favourite Rainbow Magic fairy!)

Step 3
Using the same ribbon, tie the bunch of beads, feathers and ribbons onto the ponytail band and knot to secure. Trim the ribbon to the same length as the elastic cords.

Funky headband

Did you know that you can wear this headband two ways? The fabric side looks really funky, but when I fancy adding a bit more colour to my outfit, I turn the band over to show the seven colours of the rainbow!

Ashley the Dragon Fairy
xx

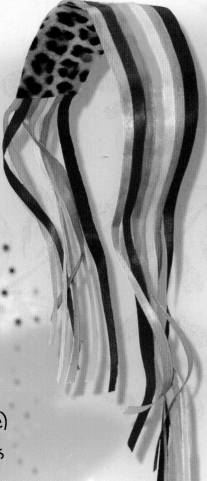

You will need:

A piece of fabric (6cm wide)

Narrow rainbow ribbons
(1 metre long)

Fabric glue

Step 1
Cut the length of fabric to fit over your head from ear to ear. Spread some glue onto the back of the fabric with a brush.

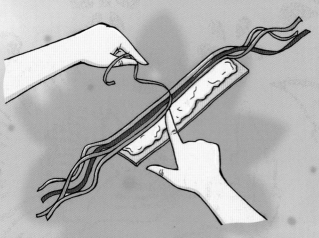

Step 2
Lay the ribbons onto the glue next to each other. Leave the same amount of extra ribbon at each end. Allow to dry.

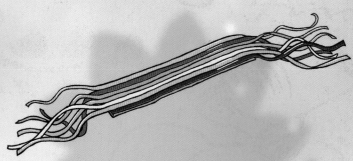

Step 3
Wear as a headband, tying the ribbons under your hair at the back. You can wear it showing the rainbow ribbon side or turn it over to show off the funky fabric.

Wonderful windmills

I love making these flowery windmills! They're great for a blustery day. The bright, spinning colours always cheer me up as they remind me of times spent playing in the sun with my Petal Fairy friends!

*Olivia
the Orchid Fairy
xx*

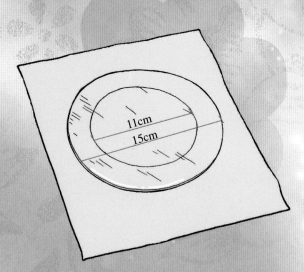

You will need:
Piece of card 15cm square
Piece of paper 10cm square
Plates, jars or egg cup to help draw
perfect circles (optional)
Pin
Bead
Pencil
Scissors

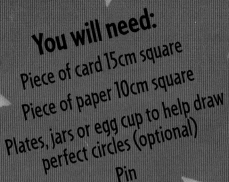

11cm
15cm

Step 1
On the piece of card, draw a circle
15cm across. Draw a smaller circle
inside the first one 11cm across.
Cut out the larger circle.

Step 2

Draw small circles between the larger and the smaller circles. These are the petals of your flower. Cut around the outer edges of the petals to make your flower.

Step 3

Fold your paper in half to make a triangle. Then fold in half again, making another triangle.

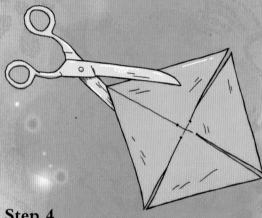

Step 4

Open the paper and mark a pencil dot on each of the folds 15mm from the centre. Cut along the folds up to the dots.

Step 5

Curl the right-hand corners of each triangle into the middle and ask a grown-up to secure all the corners with a pin through the middle of the paper.

Step 6

Now push the pin through the bead, then through the centre of your flower shape, and finally, 1cm from the top of a pencil. Blow your windmill and watch it spin!

Christmas tree decorations

Every year my friend Stella the Star Fairy flutters over to help me make these tree decorations. The shimmery shapes always get us in a Christmassy mood! Why not make the shapes gold, silver or even rainbow-coloured?

Holly
the Christmas Fairy
xx

You will need:
Coloured or patterned paper
Scissors
PVA glue
Ribbon
Selection of glitter glue, glitter, beads and sequins (optional decorations)

Step 1
Fold a piece of paper and draw one half of a star or heart. Cut it out and open up the shape. This is the template for your decoration.

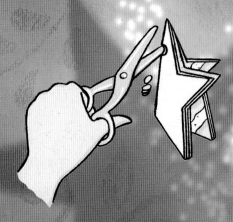

Step 2
Use the template to draw and cut out three more identical shapes. Fold each one exactly in half.

Step 3
Put all the shapes together and cut a small hole near the top.

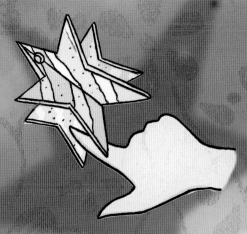

Step 4
Glue the back of one half of a shape to the back of another half, matching it as closely as possible.

Step 5
Then glue the back of the other half of the shape and do the same again. Keep doing this until all the shapes are glued together and you have a complete star. Leave to dry.

Step 6
Decorate your shapes and thread ribbon through the hole at the top to hang on your tree.

Sun and snow spellcaster

Sun or snow - which would you prefer? Each night, turn this decoration to show the fairy forecast you'd like for the next day, then hang it on your bedroom door. If you're lucky, your weather wish might just come true!

Goldie the Sunshine Fairy
xx

You will need:

2 rectangular pieces of card approximately 25 cm x 10 cm (ideally pale blue and dark blue, or card can be painted)

PVA glue

Scissors

Small bowl and egg cup (to help make perfect circles)

Paint, coloured paper, cotton wool, sequins, to decorate

Step 1

Paint the card if necessary. One piece should be pale blue and the other dark blue. Allow to dry. Stick the two pieces of card together with PVA glue. Allow these to dry.

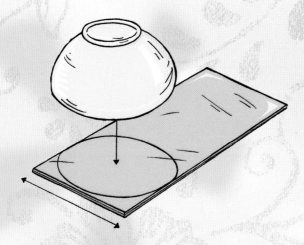

Step 2

Using the small bowl as a guide, draw an arc at the top of your card. Cut around the arc so the end of the card is rounded.

Step 3

Use an egg cup to draw a small circle near the rounded end of the card. Cut a line from the edge of the card to the small circle and cut out the small circle.

Step 4

On the pale blue side, paint a rainbow at the rounded end. Make fluffy clouds using cotton wool or white paper. Paint or glue on a sun and sunbeams.

Step 5

On the dark blue side, stick sequins and cotton wool to make snowflakes and cloudy skies. Hang the spellcaster on your doorknob and see if you can predict the weather. Will it be sunny or snowy?

Swirly dance ribbons

Easy

This ribbon wand makes me want to dance, dance, dance! The ribbons are perfect for a special performance, but are just as much fun to play with in your bedroom. Try making patterns in the air and then surround yourself in swirls – it's irresistible!

Jessica
the Jazz Fairy
xx

You will need:
2 or 3 narrow ribbons
(1 metre long)
Piece of tissue paper (30cm square)
Sticky tape
1 straw
PVA glue
Glitter to decorate (optional)

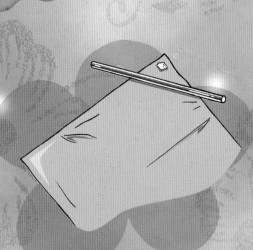

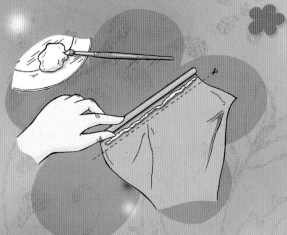

Step 1

Squeeze a pea-sized blob of glue on one corner of the tissue paper and lay a straw just below it. Wrap one layer of tissue paper tightly round the straw.

Step 2

Paint a strip of glue alongside the straw and wrap the tissue paper round again. Repeat so there are three layers of tissue paper. Cut off the extra paper.

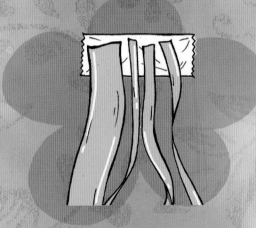

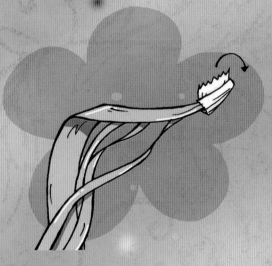

Step 3

Lay the ends of the ribbons side by side onto a piece of sticky tape.

Step 4

Roll the ribbons very tightly to make a point. Leave to dry.

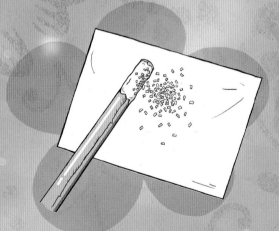

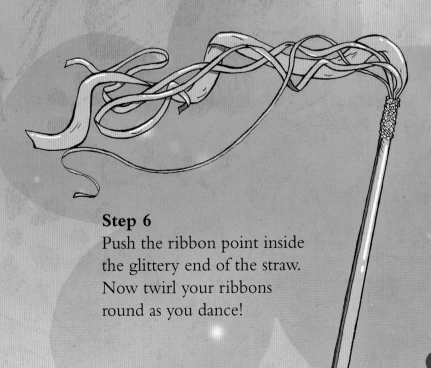

Step 5

Paint the top of the straw in PVA glue and roll in glitter. Allow to dry.

Step 6

Push the ribbon point inside the glittery end of the straw. Now twirl your ribbons round as you dance!

Fairyland tiara

I love wearing the Fairyland crown jewels and my tiara is my favourite of them all! Why not make a silvery one just like mine, and then decorate it with twinkly gems? Your headdress will be truly unique and fit for a fairy queen!

Queen Titania
xx

You will need:

Strips of aluminium foil approx 2cm wide

A thin plastic hairband

Sticky tape

Jewels or sequins to decorate your tiara (optional)

PVA glue (optional)

Step 1

Wrap the strips of foil tightly round the hairband until the hairband is completely covered with foil.

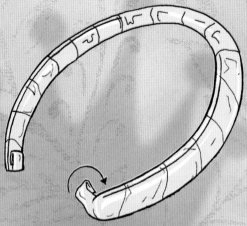

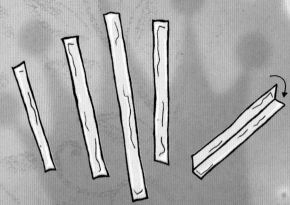

Step 2

Squeeze the ends of the foil together and tuck them under the hairband. Cut off any excess foil to make it neat and tidy.

Step 3

Cut five strips of foil: two strips 10cm long; two strips 8cm long; one strip 12cm long. Fold them in half lengthwise with the shiny side out, and then in half again.

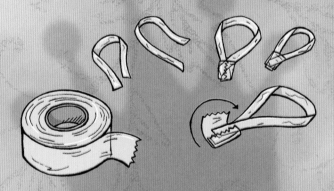

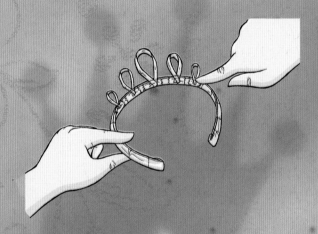

Step 4

Bend each foil strip into a loop. Stick the ends together with clear sticky tape.

Step 5

Fix the loops to the back of your tiara with sticky tape. Put the biggest loop in the middle, the medium-size loops on either side, and the smallest ones at each end.

Step 6

Stick on jewels and sequins with PVA glue to make an extra-special tiara twinkling with fairy magic.

Frosty snowglobe

This glittery globe reminds me of the ones the Rainbow Fairies gave to Kirsty and Rachel when they rescued them. The pesky pair! The icy dome will sparkle like snow every time you give it a shake.

Jack Frost

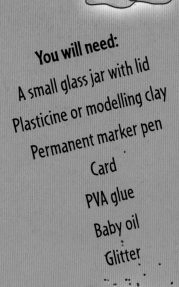

Tip

Keep the snowglobe on a saucer to protect furniture in case any oil escapes!

Step 1

Draw a picture of Jack Frost's castle onto card with permanent marker pen. (You can copy a picture from a Rainbow Magic book.) Cut out the picture. The finished shape must fit inside your jar.

You will need:

A small glass jar with lid

Plasticine or modelling clay

Permanent marker pen

Card

PVA glue

Baby oil

Glitter

Step 2

Paint the front, back and edges of the card with three or four layers of PVA glue. Leave to dry between coats.

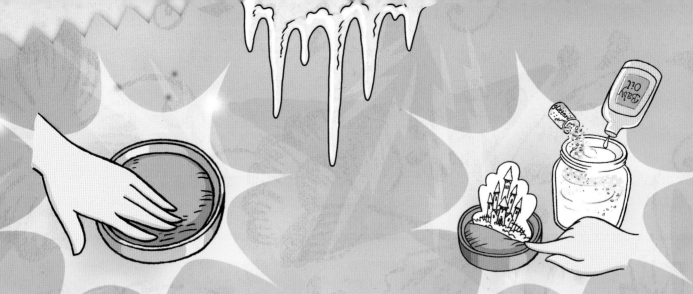

Step 3
Press modelling clay into the lid of the jar. Leave enough space around the edge so the lid still fits on the jar.

Step 4
Press your picture firmly into the clay. Fill the jar to the top with baby oil and add a good pinch of glitter.

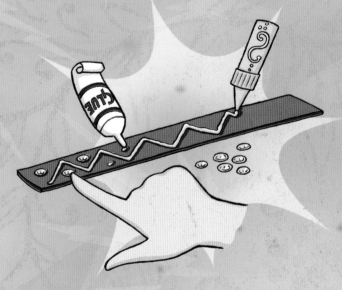

Step 5
Screw the lid tightly back onto the jar. Wipe any oil off the outside of the jar. Use a strip of modelling clay to seal the join between the jar and the lid.

Step 6
Decorate a strip of card and stick it around the rim of the lid to cover the seal.

Step 7
Give your snowglobe a shake to see a glittery snowstorm swirling round Jack Frost's castle!

Fairly easy

Perfect Pizza

These delicious fairy-sized pizzas make the perfect snack for a party! See how many delicious toppings you can pile onto each one!

Danni
the Drum Fairy
xx

You will need:
1 muffin
2 tbsp tomato-based pasta sauce
2 tbsp cheddar cheese
Toppings of your choice,
for example: sliced peppers, olives,
fresh tomatoes
or cooked sausage

Step 1
Ask a grown-up to help you slice the muffin in half. This will give you two round pizza bases.

Step 2
Cover each base with tomato pasta sauce. Add toppings, such as peppers, olives, fresh tomatoes or cooked sausage.

Step 3
Sprinkle on the cheese. Ask a grown-up to help you cook your pizzas under a medium grill for approximately five minutes until the cheese is melted and bubbling. Yummy!

Fairy heaven!

Bananas, milk and a touch of honey - what more could a fairy wish for? All my friends adore this scrummy smoothie! We sometimes add raspberries from our very own Fairyland gardens for that little extra touch.

*Chrissie
the Wish Fairy
xx*

You will need:
1 peeled sliced ripe banana
250ml chilled whole milk
1 tbsp honey
4 or 5 raspberries (optional)

Step 1
Pour the milk into a blender.

Step 2
Add the banana, and the raspberries if you have them.

Step 3
Add the honey. Then blend the ingredients until smooth. Pour into tall glasses. Add a straw and enjoy!

Goodbye!

We hope that you have enjoyed making all of these sparkly fairy things. We look forward to seeing you again very soon!

The Rainbow Magic fairies
xxx